Contents

Making marks

You can make lots of marks with a pencil.

Lines

Dots

Squiggles

Try it

Draw lines, dots and squiggles in the box.

Practise it

Draw more lines, dots and squiggles to finish the pictures.

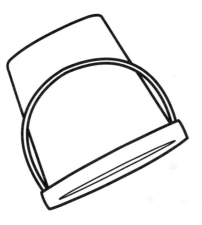

Schofield & Sims **WriteWell**

WriteWell

Schofield & Sims

Book One
Patterning

Handwriting Stage 1 | Reception

Name

Welcome to this book

The **WriteWell** series will help you to develop good handwriting habits. As you work through the series, you will learn how to improve your handwriting and develop your own style.

This is **Book 1**. In this book, you will learn to draw shapes and patterns. This will help you prepare to write the letters of the alphabet in **Books 2** and **3**.

The activities

This book is split up into 15 units. Each unit shows you a different shape or pattern. With each one, there are activities to complete. These will build your confidence until you can draw the pattern all by yourself.

When you see this style of line, use your finger to trace along it carefully.

When you see this style of line, use your pencil to trace along it carefully. Try to stay inside the blue line.

• This red dot tells you where to start. Put your finger or pencil here to begin.

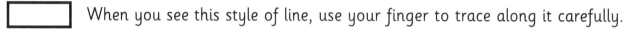 These arrows show you which direction to move your finger or pencil.

 Look out for tips and extra activity ideas from Nibs, the **WriteWell** monkey!

Checking your work

When you finish a unit, look back at your work. Do your patterns look like the example? Circle your best pattern. Which pattern could you improve?

Before you start

Check that your body is in the correct position for writing. Ask an adult to help you.

Posture ✓

Pencil grip and pressure ✓

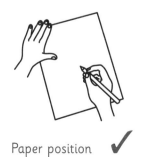

Paper position ✓

Try making marks with chalks, felt-tip pens, crayons or markers.

Draw lines, dots and squiggles to decorate the cupcakes.

Drawing lines

Lines can be straight, curved or wavy. You can draw lines right across the page. Draw lines like this.

Try it

Start at the dot. Use your finger to trace the lines.

Practise it

Start at the dot. Trace the lines with your pencil.

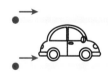

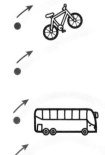

Try making straight, curved or wavy lines with wool or string.

Apply it

Draw lines on the T-shirt.

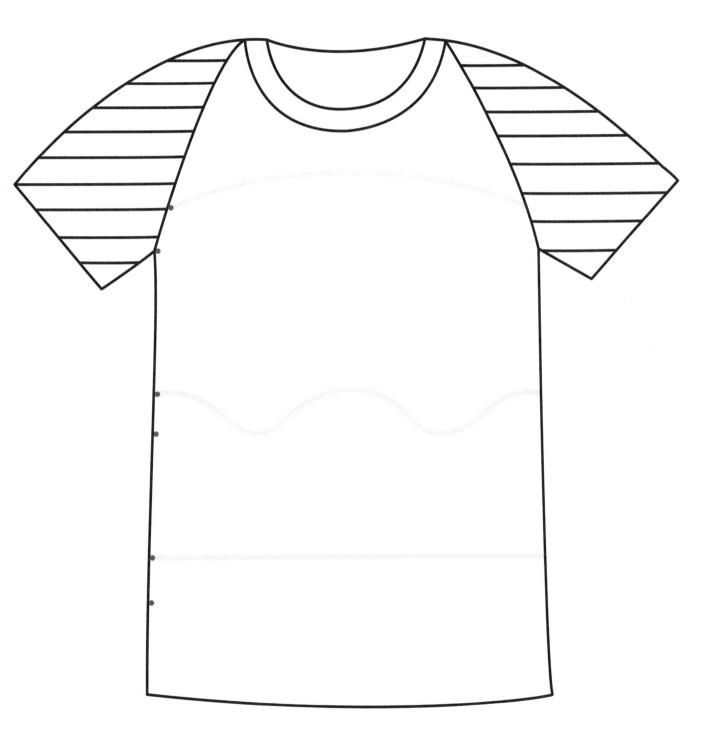

Drawing shapes

You can draw lines to make shapes. Some shapes are made up of straight lines. Some shapes are made up of curved lines.

Try it

Use your finger to trace over the shapes.

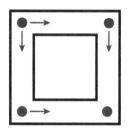 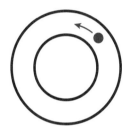 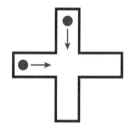

Practise it

Join the dots with your pencil to draw the shapes.

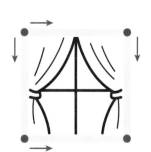  

Schofield & Sims **WriteWell**

Try drawing shapes on coloured paper and then cut them out to make a picture.

Draw shapes to make the windows on the buildings.

Straight line patterns

This pattern is made up of straight lines. All the lines start at the top and go straight down.

Try it

Use your finger to trace over the straight line pattern.

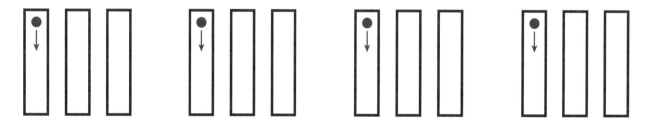

Practise it

Trace the straight line patterns with your pencil.

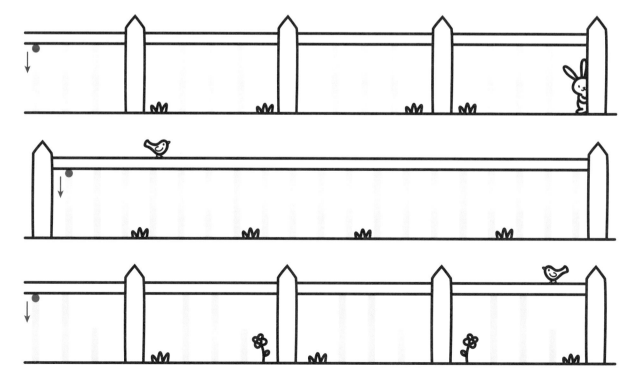

Try making a straight line pattern using paper drinking straws.

Apply it

Trace and draw straight line patterns.

More straight line patterns

This pattern is made up of straight lines. Some of the lines go down and some of the lines go across.

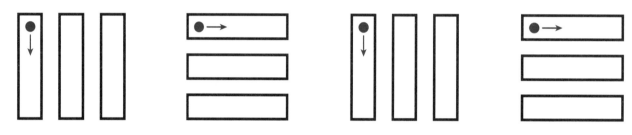

Try it

Use your finger to trace over the straight line pattern.

Practise it

Trace the straight line patterns with your pencil.

Try making straight line patterns down and across in the sand pit using a stick.

Apply it

Trace and draw straight line patterns down and across.

Circle patterns

A circle pattern is made up of round circles. Circles curve all the way round. The circles can be different sizes.

Try it

Use your finger to trace over the circle pattern.

Practise it

Trace the circle patterns with your pencil.

Try making a circle pattern using chocolate buttons or pennies.

Trace and draw circle patterns.

Curl patterns

A curl pattern is made up of little curved lines. A curl goes round like a circle but then it stops.

Use your finger to trace over the curl pattern.

Practise it

Trace the curl patterns with your pencil.

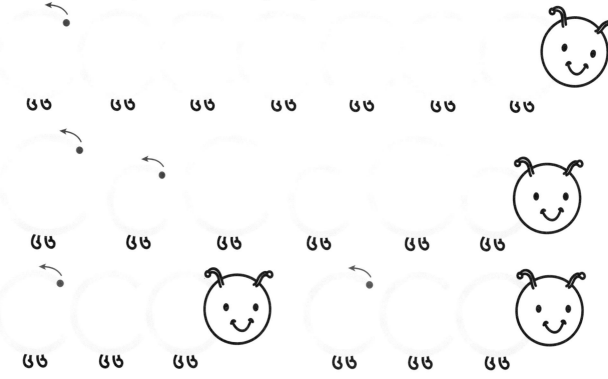

Schofield & Sims **WriteWell**

Try making a curl pattern using rolls of play dough.

Apply it

Trace and draw curl patterns.

Wave patterns

A wave pattern is made up of a line that keeps curving under. It starts at the top and goes down and up and down and up. It can go right across the page.

Try it

Use your finger to trace over the wave pattern.

Practise it

Trace the wave patterns with your pencil.

Schofield & Sims **WriteWell**

Try making a wave pattern using finger paints.

Trace and draw wave patterns.

Arch patterns

An arch pattern is made up of a line that keeps curving over.
It goes up and over and up and over and up and over.

Try it

Use your finger to trace over the arch pattern.

Practise it

Trace the arch patterns with your pencil.

Schofield & Sims **WriteWell**

Try making an arch pattern in sand or flour using your finger.

Apply it

Trace and draw arch patterns.

Loop patterns

A loop pattern has lots of curly loops. This loop pattern is made up of a line that keeps curling up and over.

Try it

Use your finger to trace over the loop pattern.

Practise it

Trace the loop patterns with your pencil.

Schofield & Sims **WriteWell**

Try making loop patterns in the air with a ribbon.

Apply it

Trace and draw loop patterns.

Spiral patterns

A spiral pattern is made up of a line that curls round and round. It can curl into the middle or out from the middle.

Try it

Use your finger to trace over the spiral pattern.

Practise it

Trace the spiral patterns with your pencil.

Schofield & Sims WriteWell

Try drawing a spiral path on the ground using chalk and then walk along it.

Apply it

Trace and draw spiral patterns.

Sloping line patterns

A sloping line pattern is made up of straight lines that lean to the side. The lines can lean forwards or backwards.

Try it

Use your finger to trace over the sloping line pattern.

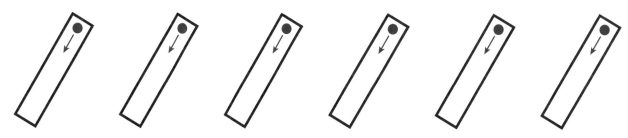

Practise it

Trace the sloping line patterns with your pencil.

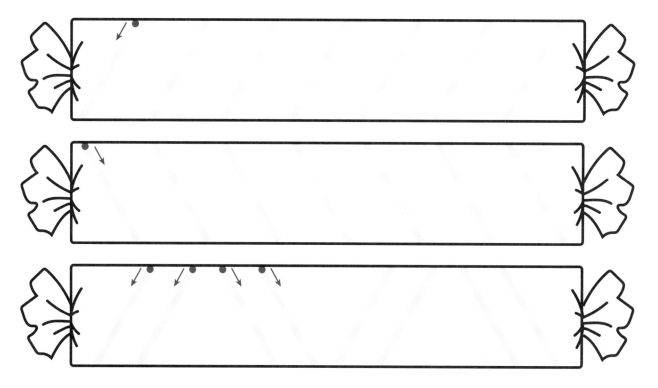

Try making a sloping line pattern with a partner using your bodies.

Apply it

Trace and draw sloping line patterns.

Zigzag patterns

A zigzag pattern is made up of sloping lines. It goes up and down and up and down.

Try it

Use your finger to trace over the zigzag pattern.

Practise it

Trace the zigzag patterns with your pencil.

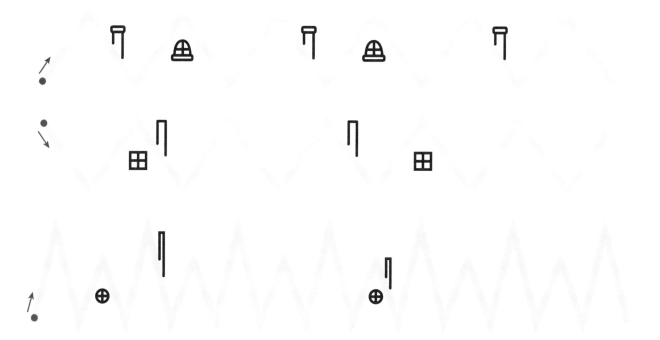

Schofield & Sims WriteWell

Try making a zigzag pattern on the
ground using sticks.

Apply it

Trace and draw zigzag patterns.

Sloping cross patterns

Two lines cross over to make each sloping cross in this pattern. One line slopes forwards and one line slopes back.

Try it

Use your finger to trace over the sloping cross pattern.

 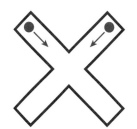  

Practise it

Trace the sloping cross patterns with your pencil.

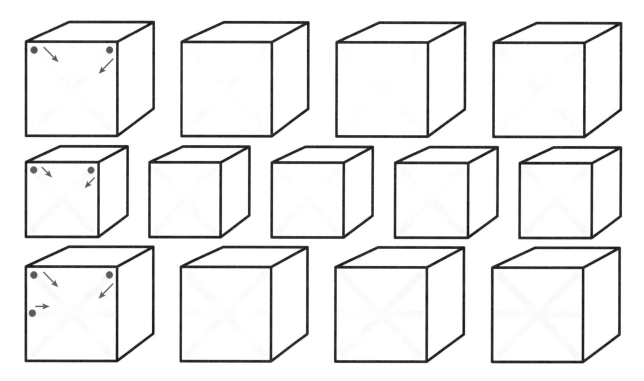

Schofield & Sims **WriteWell**

Try drawing sloping cross patterns in chalk on a board or on dark paper.

Apply it

Trace and draw sloping cross patterns.

Figures of eight

A figure of eight keeps curving round. It curves one way and then it curves back the other way and joins up.

Try it

Use your finger to trace over the figure of eight pattern.

Practise it

Trace the figure of eight patterns with your pencil.

Schofield & Sims **WriteWell**

Try making figure of eight patterns on the carpet using a toy car.

Trace and draw figure of eight patterns.

WriteWell challenge 1

Copy the picture of the shape robot. Draw the shapes as carefully as you can using the square as a starting point.

WriteWell challenge 2

Draw a different pattern on each square of the quilt. Use coloured pencils to make the patterns look bright and cheerful.

Book One
Patterning

WriteWel

Schofield & Sims WriteWell is a complete course designed to guide children from their first steps in mark-making towards the development of secure, fluent and comfortable joined handwriting that can be adapted for a range of purposes.

Handwriting is a complex process that requires the simultaneous use of cognitive, physical and perceptual skills. As development can vary greatly from child to child, **Schofield & Sims WriteWell** splits learning into manageable modules, offering you the flexibility to select the appropriate book for your child's needs. Young writers can then move through the programme at their own pace as their handwriting skills flourish – a highly personalised approach that ensures a confident foundation for every child.

This is WriteWell 1: Patterning. **In this book, children will learn to draw a range of shapes and patterns as preparation for learning to form the letters of the alphabet. This book includes 15 teaching units, each containing activities that gradually increase in difficulty, and two summative WriteWell Challenge tasks, designed to showcase new learning and encourage children to take pride in their handwriting skills.**

Stage 1
Shape

Stage 2
Space, size and sitting on the line

Stage 3
Stringing togethe and slant

Stage 4
Speed and style

Published by Schofield & Sims Ltd,
7 Mariner Court, Wakefield, West Yorkshire WF4 3FL, UK

This edition copyright © Schofield & Sims Ltd, 2019. First published in 2019

Author: Carol Matchett. Carol Matchett has asserted her moral rights under the Copyright, Designs and Patents Act, 1988, to be identified as the author of this work.

British Library Cataloguing in Publication Data
A catalogue record for this book is available from the British Library.

Design by Oxford Designers & Illustrators Ltd. Cover design by Ledgard Jepson Ltd
Printed in the UK by Page Bros (Norwich) Ltd

Schofield&Sims

For further information and to place your order visit www.schofieldandsims.co.uk or telephone 01484 607080

ISBN 978-07217-1633-6

MIX
Paper from responsible sources
FSC® C023114

ISBN 978 07217 1633 6
£3.95 (Retail price)

9 780721 716336

WriteWell

Schofield&Sims

Book Five
Letter Size and Position

Handwriting Stage 2 | Year 1

Name

Welcome to this book

The **WriteWell** series will help you to develop good handwriting habits. As you work through the series, you will learn how to improve your handwriting and develop your own style.

This is **Book 5**. Now that you can write lowercase letters, capital letters and numbers, you are ready to learn about size, position and spacing.

Size, position and spacing

In this book, you will see letters and numbers on handwriting lines like those below. This is to help you see how tall your letters should be.

Letters and numbers on the four handwriting lines

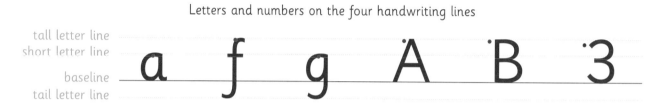

tall letter line
short letter line
baseline
tail letter line

In the first part of the book, you will practise writing letters and numbers at the correct size. Then you will learn to position letters and numbers correctly on the baseline so they do not float above or sink below it. Finally, you will start to use the correct spacing within and between words so that your writing is clear and easy to read.

Look carefully at the group of letters or numbers you are learning about and then work through the activities. At the end of the unit, you will practise using the letters or numbers in words, phrases or sentences.

Checking your work

When you finish a unit, look back at your work. Are your letters or numbers the correct size and in the correct position on the baseline? Circle your best letter or number and then choose one to improve.

Before you start

Check that your body is in the correct position for writing. Ask an adult to help you.

Posture ✔

Pencil grip and pressure ✔

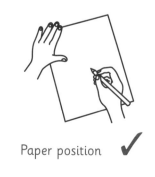

Paper position ✔